Face Painting

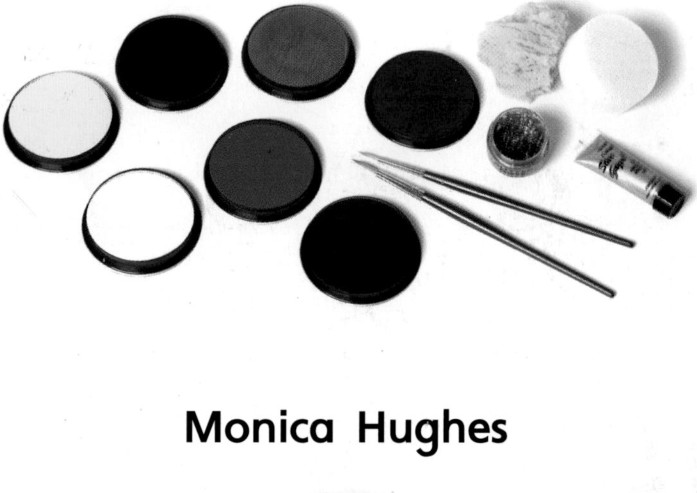

Monica Hughes

RIGBY

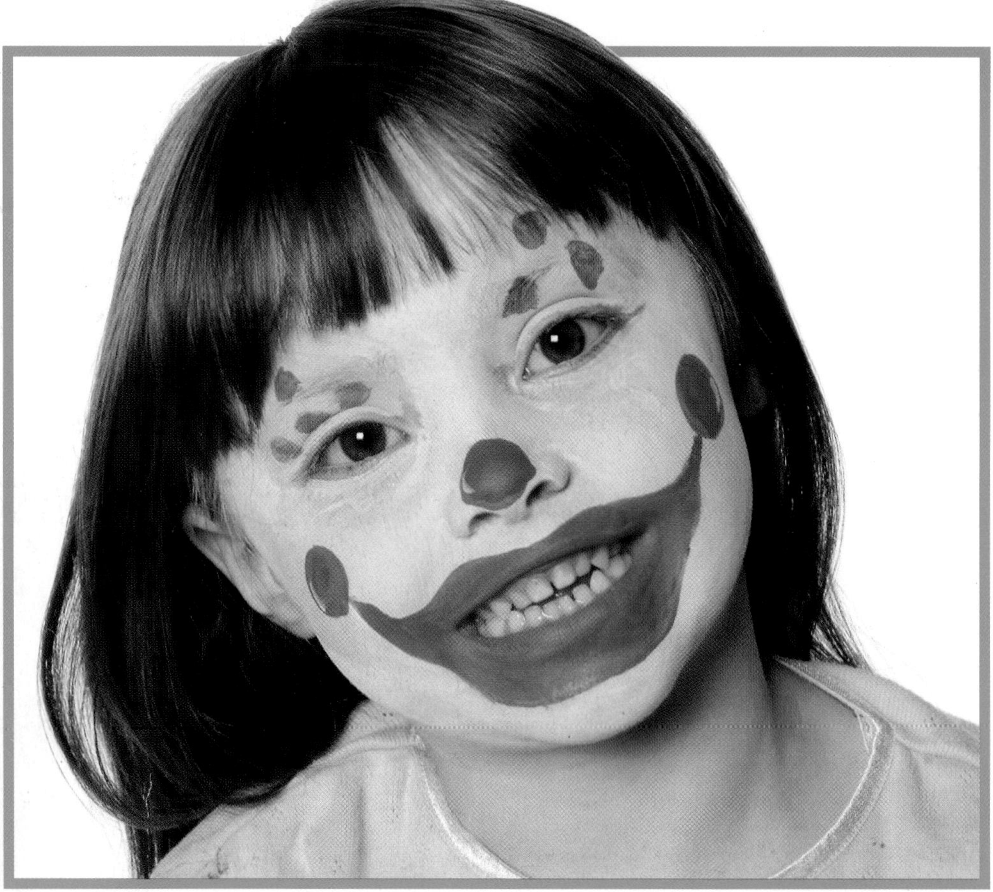

I am a clown.

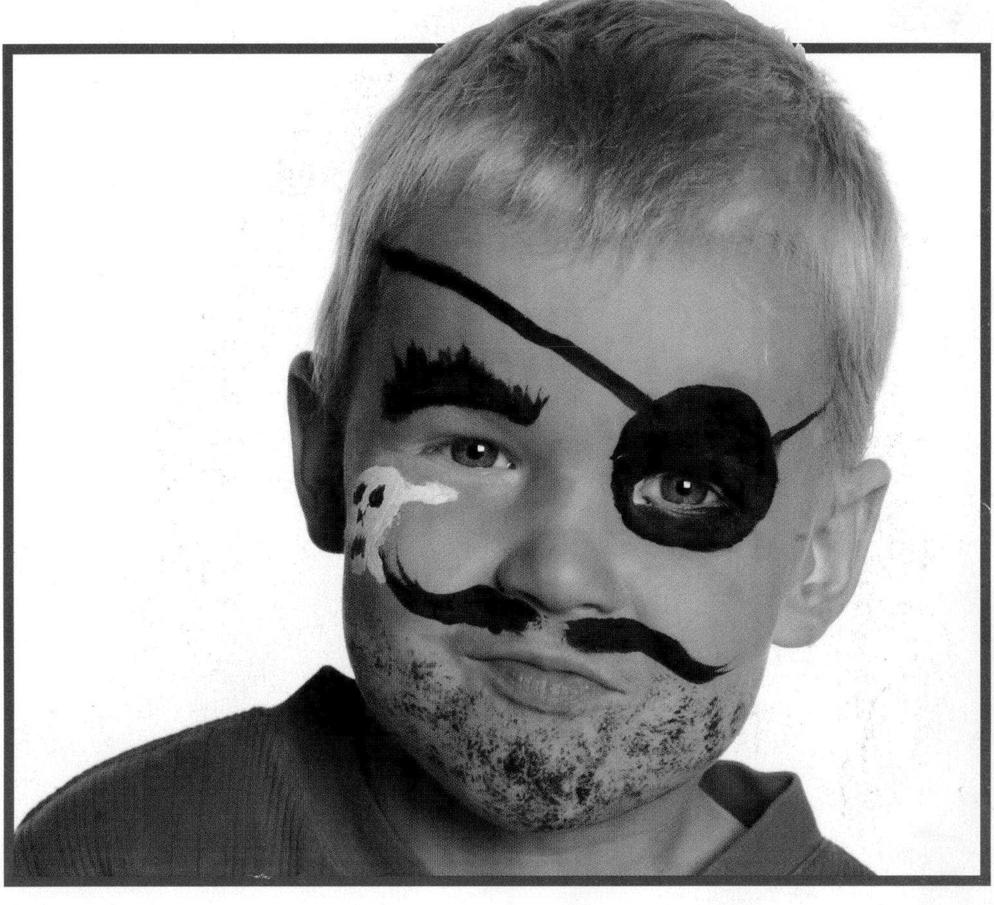

I am a pirate.

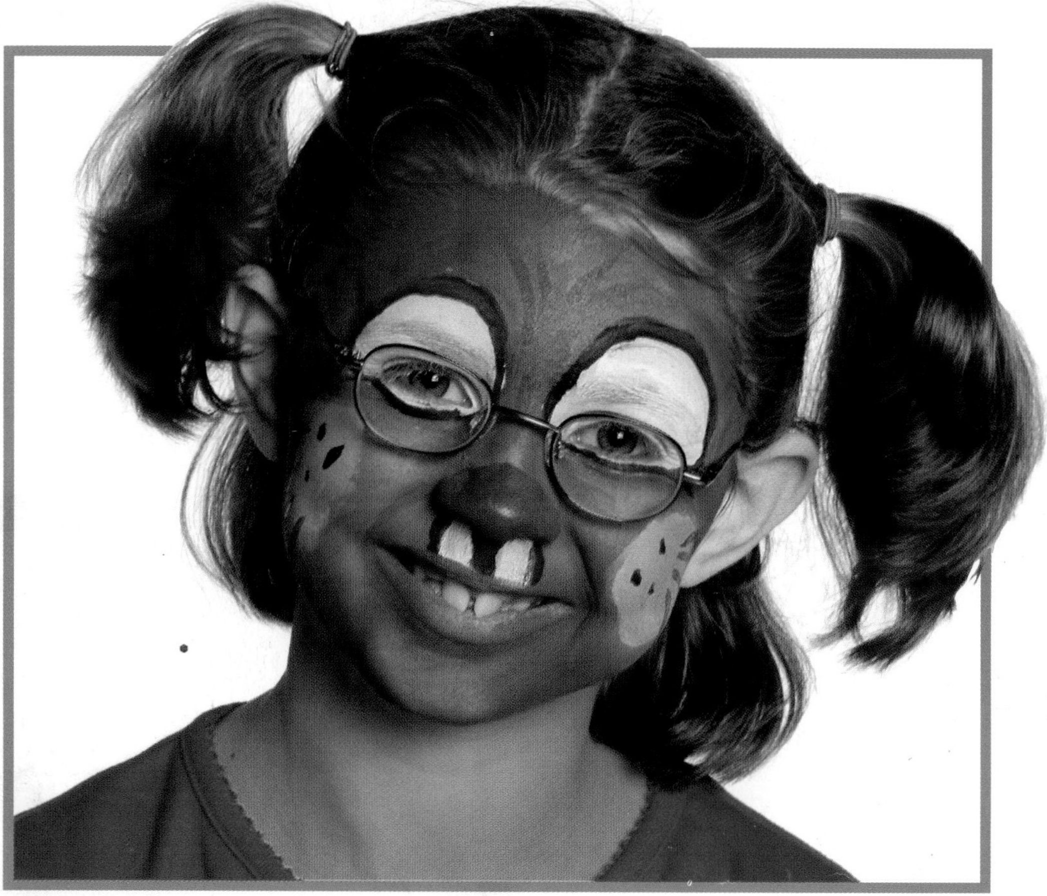

I am a rabbit.

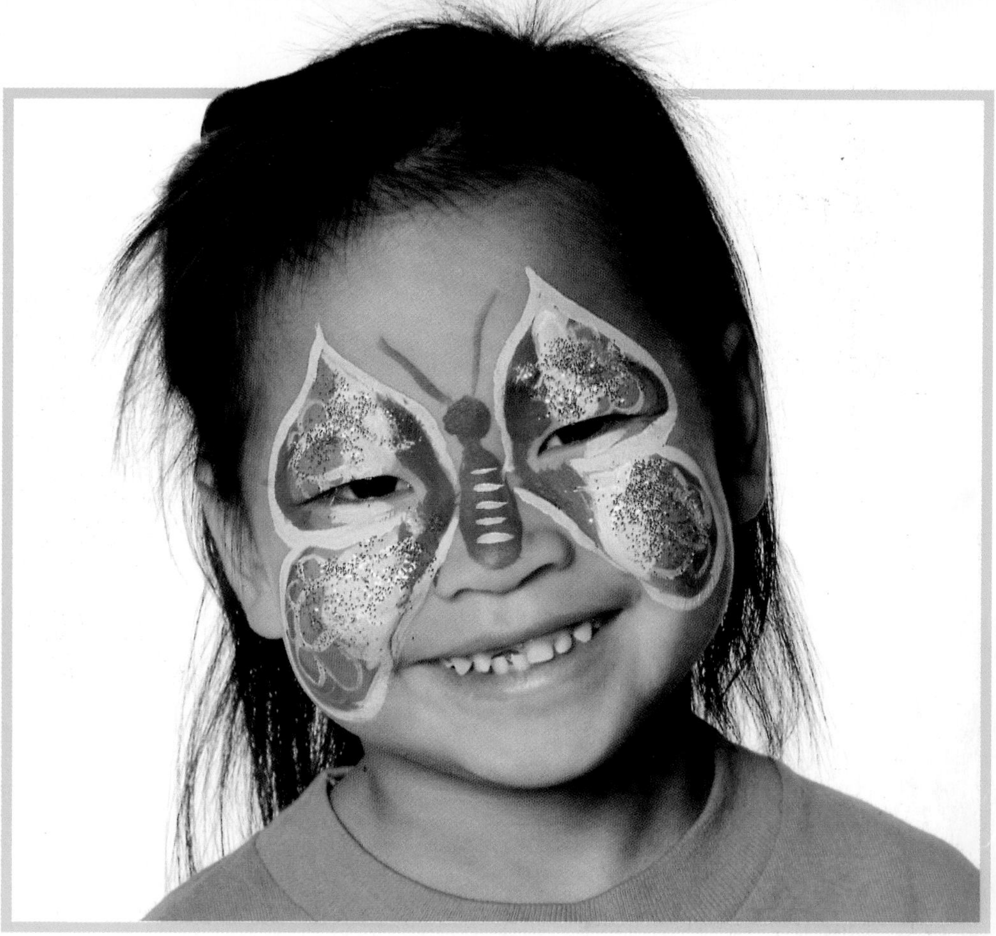

I am a butterfly.

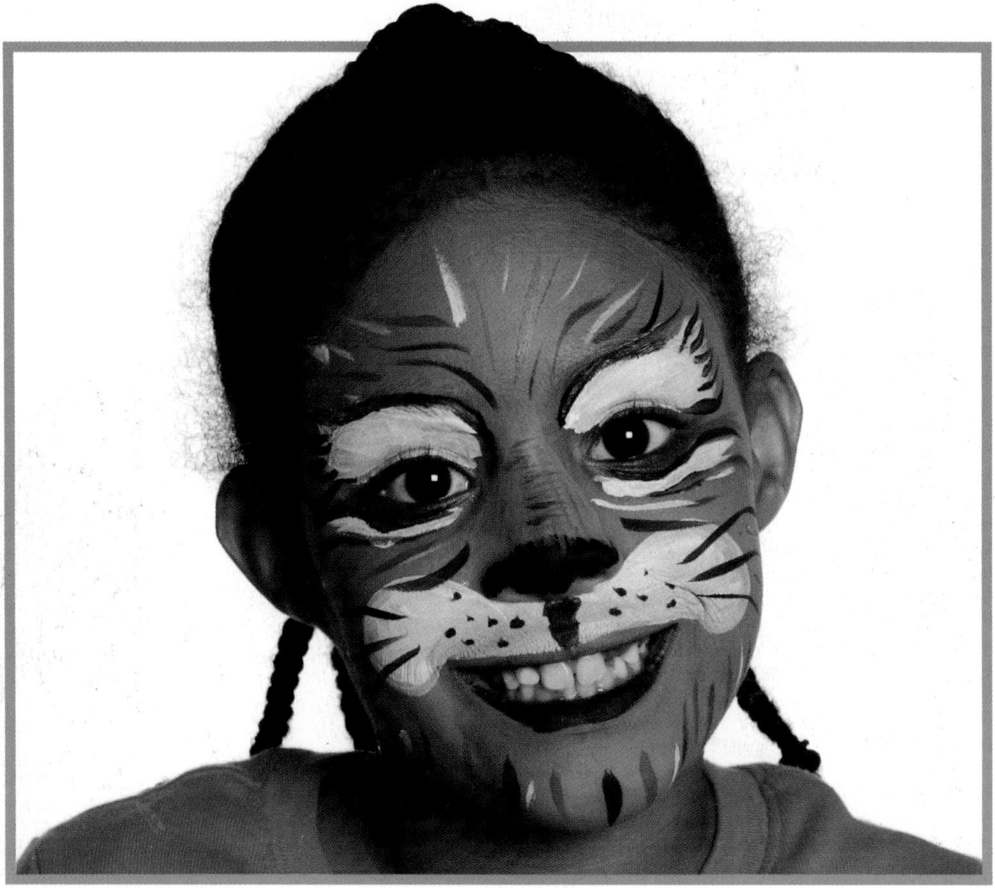

I am a tiger.

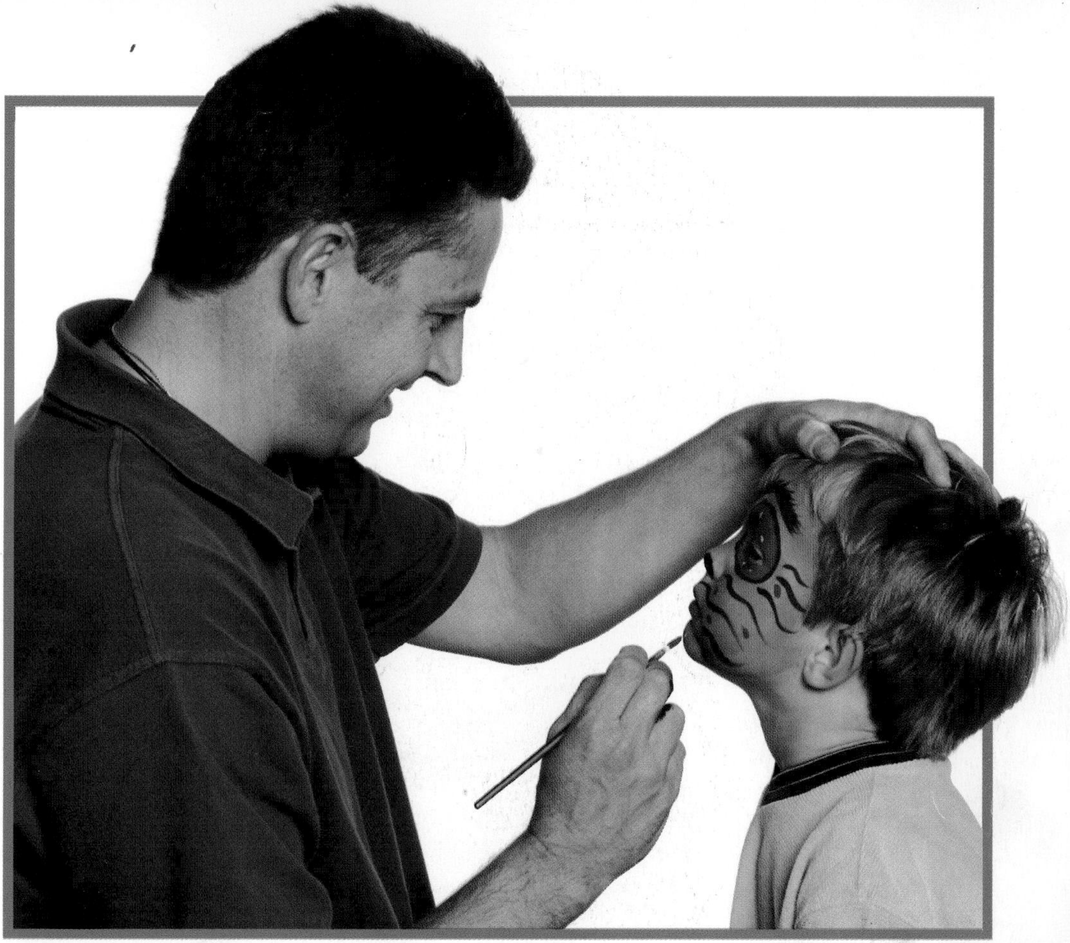

You are ...

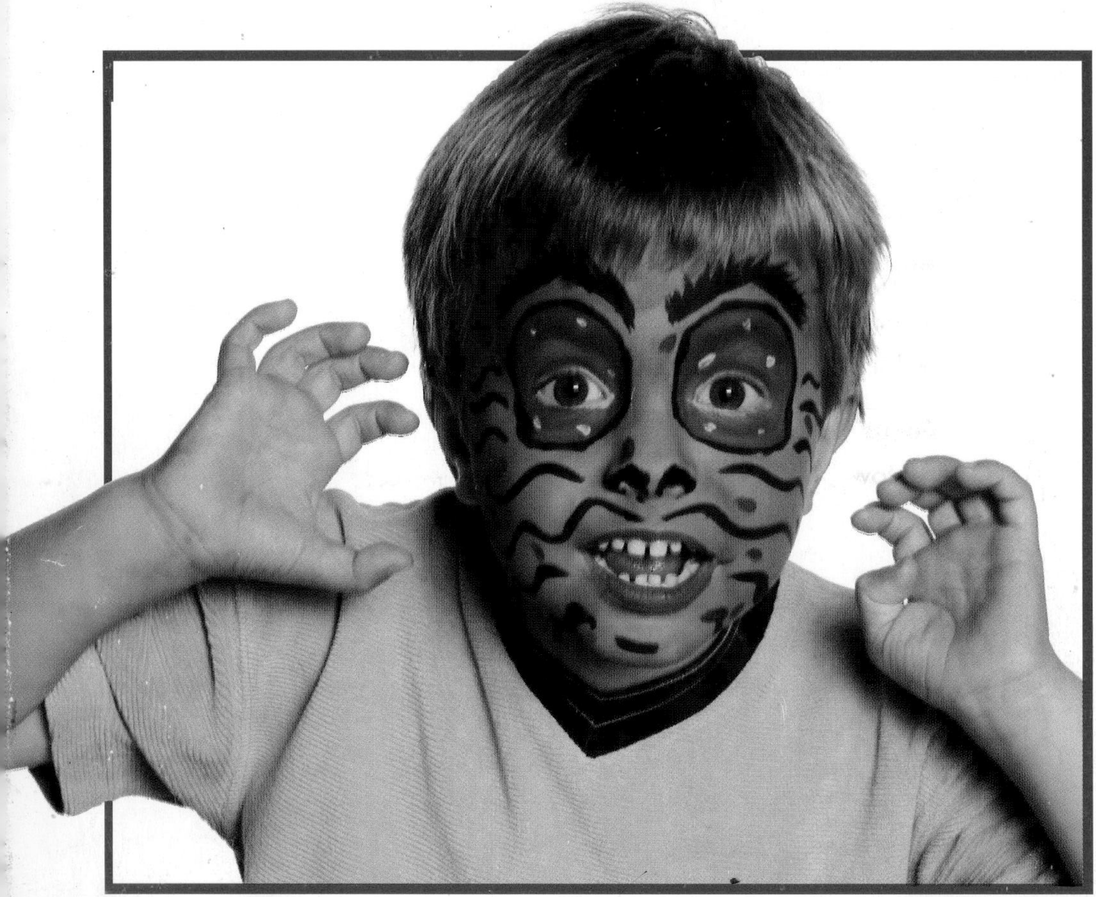

a monster!